you are strong + courageous · you are strong + courageous · you are strong + courageous · you are strong + courageous · you are strong + courageous · you are strong + courageous · you are strong + courageous · you are strong + courageous · you are strong + courageous

u are strong + courageo
courageous · you are str
u are strong + courageo
courageous · you are st
ou are strong + courage
+ courageous · you are st
you are strong + courag
+ courageous · you are s
you are strong + courag
+ courageous · you are
you are strong + courag
g + courageous · you are

To _____

From _____

Date _____

Inspirational Productivity Journal

YOU ARE STRONG & COURAGEOUS

Melissa Horvath

DaySpring

LIVE YOUR FAITH

Hey there, friend!

I'm Melissa Horvath, Owner and Designer of the home décor and gift company Sweet Water Decor. As a busy mom of three, wife, and business owner, I've been inspired by God to motivate and inspire, not only through my products, but also through books, journals, and more. In my devotional *You Got This*, I equip and encourage you to pursue your God-given purpose. Then in my devotional *Go for It*, I help you boldly live out the life God created for you. Now, in this *Inspirational Productivity Journal: Strong and Courageous*, I will inspire and help you to lean into the Lord each day while giving yourself grace and walking in courage.

As women we live busy lives, and we can often forget that God is cheering us on along the way. He created us and knew us before we were born, and He has so many wonderful purposes and plans for our lives. We can easily get caught up in our day-to-day lives and forget that we are a daughter of the King and we are worthy!

I'm here to walk alongside you each day for ten weeks as we grow closer to God and understand ourselves more. Each week, you'll have the opportunity to set some dreams and goals for yourself, to identify three important tasks you want to accomplish, to plan something fun for the week, and to utilize a habit tracker.

Each day you'll record your to-do list, top priorities, and what you're grateful for, and then you will release any tension, worry, anxiety, stress, and more to God. You'll also write down three things you need to give to God that day and really release them along with what your top prayer needs are for the day.

Last, you will celebrate a WIN for each day, no matter how big or how small it is! It can be as simple as enjoying a conversation with a friend or appreciating that first sip of morning coffee.

I hope that by the end of the ten weeks, that you feel encouraged, closer to the Lord and yourself, and stronger and more courageous to tackle each day! Are you ready to get started? Maybe you could even pick up an extra copy or two and invite some friends to join you so you can hold each other accountable and grow stronger and more courageous together!

One final tip before you start: never feel like you have to complete everything each day or each week. Remember, this is for YOU! Make it your own—change the prompts as you see fit and make adjustments—and stay encouraged! I'm excited for you to dive in!

See ya on the next page!

melissa

Follow along on Instagram
@melissa_horvath_ and
@sweetwaterdecor

Personal

_____
_____
_____
_____

Spiritual

_____
_____
_____
_____

Financial

_____
_____
_____
_____

Relationships

_____
_____
_____
_____

Health/Fitness

_____
_____
_____
_____

Career

Academic

Good habits to make

Scriptures to memorize

What Impact Will Achieving These Goals Have On you?

_____
_____
_____
_____
_____
_____
_____
_____
_____
_____
_____
_____
_____
_____
_____
_____
_____
_____
_____
_____
_____
_____
_____

make the most of your Time

- ☐ _____
- ☐ _____
- ☐ _____
- ☐ _____
- ☐ _____
- ☐ _____
- ☐ _____

Knowing Your Worth

Your worth isn't found in what you accomplish, in your title or labels, or in what you think others think of you; it's found in Jesus! Practice giving yourself grace this week, especially when you start to feel rushed or overwhelmed by trying to live up to the expectations you set for yourself or others have set for you. Just take a moment to breathe, then put things back in place. You are a daughter of the King! You have no one to please. He loves you just the way He designed you to be, and He wants you to replace the worry and the striving with happiness and knowing He loves you no matter what! Remember, your worth isn't in what you accomplish or in what others think of you—it's found in Jesus! Practice giving yourself grace this week.

habit tracker

HABIT	GOAL	MON	TUE	WED	THU	FRI	SAT	SUN

what are your dreams +
goals this week?

_____
_____
_____
_____
_____
_____
_____

top 3 tasks for
the week ahead

1 _____
2 _____
3 _____

what is something fun
you are looking forward
to this week?

_____
_____
_____
_____
_____
_____

Today Is Your Day

The Lord is my light and my salvation; whom shall I fear?
The Lord is the stronghold of my life; of whom shall I be afraid?
PSALM 27:1

I am grateful for...

_____
_____
_____
_____
_____

to-do list

- ☐ _____
- ☐ _____
- ☐ _____
- ☐ _____
- ☐ _____
- ☐ _____
- ☐ _____
- ☐ _____
- ☐ _____
- ☐ _____
- ☐ _____
- ☐ _____

top priorities

_____
_____
_____
_____
_____
_____
_____
_____
_____
_____
_____

three things I need to
give to God today...

1 _____
2 _____
3 _____

my prayer today is...

_____
_____
_____
_____
_____
_____
_____
_____
_____
_____
_____

what is your "win" today?

_____
_____
_____
_____
_____

Today Is Your Day

"For I know the plans I have for you," declares the LORD,
"plans to prosper you and not to harm you,
plans to give you hope and a future."
JEREMIAH 29:11 NIV

I am grateful for...

_____
_____
_____
_____
_____

to-do list

- ☐ _____
- ☐ _____
- ☐ _____
- ☐ _____
- ☐ _____
- ☐ _____
- ☐ _____
- ☐ _____
- ☐ _____
- ☐ _____
- ☐ _____
- ☐ _____

top priorities

_____
_____
_____
_____
_____
_____
_____
_____
_____
_____
_____

three things I need to
give to God today...

1 _____
2 _____
3 _____

my prayer today is...

_____
_____
_____
_____
_____
_____
_____
_____
_____
_____
_____

what is your "win" today?

_____
_____
_____
_____

Today Is Your Day

The steadfast love of the LORD never ceases;
his mercies never come to an end; they are new every morning;
great is your faithfulness.
LAMENTATIONS 3:22–23

I am grateful for...

to-do list

- ☐ _____
- ☐ _____
- ☐ _____
- ☐ _____
- ☐ _____
- ☐ _____
- ☐ _____
- ☐ _____
- ☐ _____
- ☐ _____
- ☐ _____
- ☐ _____

top priorities

three things I need to
give to God today...

1 _____
2 _____
3 _____

my prayer today is...

_____
_____
_____
_____
_____
_____
_____
_____
_____
_____
_____

what is your "win" today?

_____
_____
_____
_____

Today Is Your Day

For you formed my inward parts; you knitted me together in my
mother's womb. I praise you, for I am fearfully and wonderfully made.
Wonderful are your works; my soul knows it very well.
PSALM 139:13–14

I am grateful for...

_____

_____

_____

_____

_____

to-do list

- [ ] _____
- [ ] _____
- [ ] _____
- [ ] _____
- [ ] _____
- [ ] _____
- [ ] _____
- [ ] _____
- [ ] _____
- [ ] _____
- [ ] _____
- [ ] _____

top priorities

_____

_____

_____

_____

_____

_____

_____

_____

_____

three things I need to
give to God today...

1 _____
2 _____
3 _____

my prayer today is...

_____
_____
_____
_____
_____
_____
_____
_____
_____
_____
_____

what is your "win" today?

_____
_____
_____
_____
_____

Today Is Your Day

Be kind to one another, tenderhearted,
forgiving one another, as God in Christ forgave you.
EPHESIANS 4:32

I am grateful for...

_____

_____

_____

_____

_____

to-do list

- [ ] _____
- [ ] _____
- [ ] _____
- [ ] _____
- [ ] _____
- [ ] _____
- [ ] _____
- [ ] _____
- [ ] _____
- [ ] _____
- [ ] _____
- [ ] _____

top priorities

_____

_____

_____

_____

_____

_____

_____

_____

_____

_____

three things I need to
give to God today...

1
2
3

my prayer today is...

what is your "win" today?

Today Is Your Day

And he said to them, "Why are you afraid, O you of little faith?"
Then he rose and rebuked the winds and the sea,
and there was a great calm.
MATTHEW 8:26

I am grateful for...

_____
_____
_____
_____
_____

to-do list

- ☐ _____
- ☐ _____
- ☐ _____
- ☐ _____
- ☐ _____
- ☐ _____
- ☐ _____
- ☐ _____
- ☐ _____
- ☐ _____
- ☐ _____
- ☐ _____

top priorities

_____
_____
_____
_____
_____
_____
_____
_____
_____
_____

three things I need to
give to God today...

1 _____
2 _____
3 _____

my prayer today is...

_____
_____
_____
_____
_____
_____
_____
_____
_____
_____

what is your "win" today?

_____
_____
_____
_____

23

Today Is Your Day

Search me, O God, and know my heart!
Try me and know my thoughts! And see if there be any
grievous way in me, and lead me in the way everlasting!
PSALM 139:23–24

I am grateful for...

_____
_____
_____
_____
_____

to-do list

- [ ] _____
- [ ] _____
- [ ] _____
- [ ] _____
- [ ] _____
- [ ] _____
- [ ] _____
- [ ] _____
- [ ] _____
- [ ] _____
- [ ] _____
- [ ] _____

top priorities

_____
_____
_____
_____
_____
_____
_____
_____
_____

three things I need to
give to God today...

1 _____
2 _____
3 _____

my prayer today is...

_____
_____
_____
_____
_____
_____
_____
_____
_____
_____

what is your "win" today?

_____
_____
_____
_____

be you.
do you.
for you.

Embracing Peace

This week, let peace and calm in. Take the pressure off yourself to be perfect and to please everyone. That's something you can never accomplish. Perfection isn't attainable or sustainable. Allow yourself to receive grace, and allow "failure" to happen. Remember, you can only control yourself, not your situations. Things don't always have to go as planned, but trust that they will go how they should. Don't forget that God's plan is better than ours. Release the internal and external pressure by taking a deep, cleansing breath. You are more than what you strive to be. As you exhale, let go of your expectations and hold on to Jesus. You have been wonderfully made to be just who you are—imperfections and all! You are the only you there will ever be, and God knew you before you were born. You've been given this day, and you'll never get this day again; so soak it all in and enjoy what you're doing—even the mundane tasks. You've got this!

habit tracker

HABIT	GOAL	MON	TUE	WED	THU	FRI	SAT	SUN

what are your dreams +
goals this week?

_____
_____
_____
_____
_____
_____

top 3 tasks for
the week ahead

1 _____
2 _____
3 _____

what is something fun
you are looking forward
to this week?

_____
_____
_____
_____
_____
_____

Today Is Your Day

For am I now seeking the approval of man, or of God?
Or am I trying to please man? If I were still trying to please man,
I would not be a servant of Christ.

GALATIANS 1:10

I am grateful for...

_____
_____
_____
_____
_____

to-do list

- [ ] _____
- [ ] _____
- [ ] _____
- [ ] _____
- [ ] _____
- [ ] _____
- [ ] _____
- [ ] _____
- [ ] _____
- [ ] _____
- [ ] _____
- [ ] _____

top priorities

_____
_____
_____
_____
_____
_____
_____
_____
_____
_____
_____

three things I need to
give to God today...

1 _____
2 _____
3 _____

my prayer today is...

_____
_____
_____
_____
_____
_____
_____
_____
_____
_____
_____

what is your "win" today?

_____
_____
_____
_____

Today Is Your Day

"Fear not, for I am with you; be not dismayed,
for I am your God; I will strengthen you, I will help you,
I will uphold you with my righteous right hand."
ISAIAH 41:10

I am grateful for...

_____
_____
_____
_____
_____

to-do list

- ☐ _____
- ☐ _____
- ☐ _____
- ☐ _____
- ☐ _____
- ☐ _____
- ☐ _____
- ☐ _____
- ☐ _____
- ☐ _____
- ☐ _____
- ☐ _____

top priorities

_____
_____
_____
_____
_____
_____
_____
_____
_____

three things I need to
give to God today...

1
2
3

my prayer today is...

what is your "win" today?

Today Is Your Day

"I have said these things to you, that in me you may have peace.
In the world you will have tribulation.
But take heart; I have overcome the world."

I am grateful for...

_____

_____

_____

_____

_____

to-do list

- [ ] _____
- [ ] _____
- [ ] _____
- [ ] _____
- [ ] _____
- [ ] _____
- [ ] _____
- [ ] _____
- [ ] _____
- [ ] _____
- [ ] _____
- [ ] _____

top priorities

_____

_____

_____

_____

_____

_____

_____

_____

_____

three things I need to
give to God today...

1 _____
2 _____
3 _____

my prayer today is...

_____
_____
_____
_____
_____
_____
_____
_____
_____
_____

what is your "win" today?

_____
_____
_____
_____

Today Is Your Day

Be on your guard; stand firm in the faith;
be courageous; be strong.
I CORINTHIANS 16:13 NIV

I am grateful for...

_____
_____
_____
_____
_____

to-do list

- [ ] _____
- [ ] _____
- [ ] _____
- [ ] _____
- [ ] _____
- [ ] _____
- [ ] _____
- [ ] _____
- [ ] _____
- [ ] _____
- [ ] _____
- [ ] _____

top priorities

_____
_____
_____
_____
_____
_____
_____
_____
_____
_____
_____

three things I need to
give to God today...

1
2
3

my prayer today is...

what is your "win" today?

Today Is Your Day

May the God of hope fill you with all joy
and peace in believing, so that by the power
of the Holy Spirit you may abound in hope.
ROMANS 15:13

I am grateful for...

_____
_____
_____
_____
_____

to-do list

- [ ] _____
- [ ] _____
- [ ] _____
- [ ] _____
- [ ] _____
- [ ] _____
- [ ] _____
- [ ] _____
- [ ] _____
- [ ] _____
- [ ] _____
- [ ] _____

top priorities

_____
_____
_____
_____
_____
_____
_____
_____

three things I need to
give to God today...

1 _____
2 _____
3 _____

my prayer today is...

_____
_____
_____
_____
_____
_____
_____
_____
_____
_____
_____
_____

what is your "win" today?

_____
_____
_____
_____

Today Is Your Day

And we know that for those who love God
all things work together for good,
for those who are called according to his purpose.
ROMANS 8:28

I am grateful for...

_____
_____
_____
_____
_____

to-do list

- ☐ _____
- ☐ _____
- ☐ _____
- ☐ _____
- ☐ _____
- ☐ _____
- ☐ _____
- ☐ _____
- ☐ _____
- ☐ _____
- ☐ _____
- ☐ _____

top priorities

_____
_____
_____
_____
_____
_____
_____
_____
_____
_____

three things I need to
give to God today...

1
2
3

my prayer today is...

what is your "win" today?

Today Is Your Day

Finally, brothers, whatever is true, whatever is honorable, whatever is just, whatever is pure, whatever is lovely, whatever is commendable, if there is any excellence, if there is anything worthy of praise, think about these things. What you have learned and received and heard and seen in me—practice these things, and the God of peace will be with you.
PHILIPPIANS 4:8–9

I am grateful for...

_____

_____

_____

_____

_____

to-do list

☐ _____
☐ _____
☐ _____
☐ _____
☐ _____
☐ _____
☐ _____
☐ _____
☐ _____
☐ _____

top priorities

_____
_____
_____
_____
_____
_____
_____
_____
_____

three things I need to
give to God today...

1 _____
2 _____
3 _____

my prayer today is...

_____
_____
_____
_____
_____
_____
_____
_____
_____
_____
_____

what is your "win" today?

_____
_____
_____
_____

you are
exactly
where you
need to be

Walking in Courage

This week, be courageous and do something out of the ordinary each day. It could be trying a new class, waking up early to get a few extra things done, calling an old friend, helping a neighbor, buying coffee for the person in line behind you . . . the possibilities are endless! As you do things for others, do so without needing praise from them or letting them know it was you. You may find a new routine or something that not only brings you joy but also brings joy to others. If you slip into your old routine for a day or two, give yourself grace and pick it back up the next day. Embrace the adventure of walking in courage every day!

habit tracker

HABIT	GOAL	MON	TUE	WED	THU	FRI	SAT	SUN

what are your dreams +
goals this week?

_____
_____
_____
_____
_____
_____

top 3 tasks for
the week ahead

1 _____
2 _____
3 _____

what is something fun
you are looking forward
to this week?

_____
_____
_____
_____
_____
_____

Today Is Your Day

Trust in the LORD with all your heart, and do not lean on
your own understanding. In all your ways acknowledge him,
and he will make straight your paths.
PROVERBS 3:5–6

I am grateful for...

_____
_____
_____
_____
_____

to-do list

- ☐ _____
- ☐ _____
- ☐ _____
- ☐ _____
- ☐ _____
- ☐ _____
- ☐ _____
- ☐ _____
- ☐ _____
- ☐ _____
- ☐ _____
- ☐ _____

top priorities

_____
_____
_____
_____
_____
_____
_____
_____
_____

three things I need to
give to God today...

1
2
3

my prayer today is...

what is your "win" today?

Today Is Your Day

And whatever you do, in word or deed,
do everything in the name of the Lord Jesus,
giving thanks to God the Father through him.
COLOSSIANS 3:17

I am grateful for...

_____
_____
_____
_____
_____

to-do list

- ☐ _____
- ☐ _____
- ☐ _____
- ☐ _____
- ☐ _____
- ☐ _____
- ☐ _____
- ☐ _____
- ☐ _____
- ☐ _____
- ☐ _____
- ☐ _____

top priorities

_____
_____
_____
_____
_____
_____
_____
_____
_____
_____

three things I need to
give to God today...

1 _____
2 _____
3 _____

my prayer today is...

_____
_____
_____
_____
_____
_____
_____
_____
_____
_____
_____
_____
_____

what is your "win" today?

_____
_____
_____
_____

Today Is Your Day

"Before I formed you in the womb I knew you,
and before you were born I consecrated you."
JEREMIAH 1:5

I am grateful for...

_____

_____

_____

_____

_____

to-do list

- ☐ _____
- ☐ _____
- ☐ _____
- ☐ _____
- ☐ _____
- ☐ _____
- ☐ _____
- ☐ _____
- ☐ _____
- ☐ _____
- ☐ _____
- ☐ _____

top priorities

_____

_____

_____

_____

_____

_____

_____

_____

_____

_____

_____

three things I need to
give to God today...

1 _____
2 _____
3 _____

my prayer today is...

_____
_____
_____
_____
_____
_____
_____
_____
_____
_____
_____

what is your "win" today?

_____
_____
_____
_____

Today Is Your Day

I will instruct you and teach you in the way you should go;
I will counsel you with my eye upon you.
PSALM 32:8

I am grateful for...

_____
_____
_____
_____
_____

to-do list

- ☐ _____
- ☐ _____
- ☐ _____
- ☐ _____
- ☐ _____
- ☐ _____
- ☐ _____
- ☐ _____
- ☐ _____
- ☐ _____
- ☐ _____
- ☐ _____

top priorities

_____
_____
_____
_____
_____
_____
_____
_____
_____
_____
_____
_____

three things I need to
give to God today...

1 _____
2 _____
3 _____

my prayer today is...

_____
_____
_____
_____
_____
_____
_____
_____
_____
_____
_____

what is your "win" today?

_____
_____
_____
_____

Today Is Your Day

Give thanks in all circumstances;
for this is God's will for you in Christ Jesus.
I THESSALONIANS 5:18 NIV

I am grateful for...

_____
_____
_____
_____
_____

to-do list

- [ ] _____
- [ ] _____
- [ ] _____
- [ ] _____
- [ ] _____
- [ ] _____
- [ ] _____
- [ ] _____
- [ ] _____
- [ ] _____
- [ ] _____
- [ ] _____

top priorities

_____
_____
_____
_____
_____
_____
_____
_____
_____
_____

three things I need to
give to God today...

1 _____
2 _____
3 _____

my prayer today is...

_____
_____
_____
_____
_____
_____
_____
_____
_____
_____
_____

what is your "win" today?

_____
_____
_____
_____

Today Is Your Day

At the right time, I, the LORD, will make it happen.
ISAIAH 60:22 NLT

I am grateful for...

_____
_____
_____
_____
_____

to-do list

- [ ] _____
- [ ] _____
- [ ] _____
- [ ] _____
- [ ] _____
- [ ] _____
- [ ] _____
- [ ] _____
- [ ] _____
- [ ] _____
- [ ] _____
- [ ] _____

top priorities

_____
_____
_____
_____
_____
_____
_____
_____
_____
_____

three things I need to
give to God today...

1 _____
2 _____
3 _____

my prayer today is...

_____
_____
_____
_____
_____
_____
_____
_____
_____
_____

what is your "win" today?

_____
_____
_____
_____

Today Is Your Day

Yet I am always with You. You hold me by my right hand.
PSALM 73:23 NLV

I am grateful for...

_____
_____
_____
_____
_____

to-do list

☐ _____
☐ _____
☐ _____
☐ _____
☐ _____
☐ _____
☐ _____
☐ _____
☐ _____
☐ _____
☐ _____
☐ _____

top priorities

_____
_____
_____
_____
_____
_____
_____
_____

three things I need to
give to God today...

1 _____
2 _____
3 _____

my prayer today is...

_____
_____
_____
_____
_____
_____
_____
_____
_____
_____

what is your "win" today?

_____
_____
_____
_____

she sees
possibility
everywhere

Focused on Jesus

Sometimes our days can be interrupted by something that causes us to worry, feel anxious, or hang on to words or actions that steal our happiness. I want you to become aware when this happens and let God's voice be louder than the world's. There will be days when circumstances or even people try to steal your joy, but remember that God's plans for you are best—and that includes not being weighed down by worry or stress but enjoying each day to the fullest. Be strong this week, and focus on Him rather than anything that may shake you or distract you from His best for you. No matter the stresses that come your way, focus on the positive this week, and know God is right by your side.

habit tracker

HABIT	GOAL	MON	TUE	WED	THU	FRI	SAT	SUN

what are your dreams + goals this week?

_____
_____
_____
_____
_____
_____
_____

top 3 tasks for the week ahead

1 _____
2 _____
3 _____

what is something fun you are looking forward to this week?

_____
_____
_____
_____
_____
_____

Today Is Your Day

I can do all things through Christ
because He gives me strength.
PHILIPPIANS 4:13 ICB

I am grateful for...

_____

_____

_____

_____

_____

to-do list

- ☐ _____
- ☐ _____
- ☐ _____
- ☐ _____
- ☐ _____
- ☐ _____
- ☐ _____
- ☐ _____
- ☐ _____
- ☐ _____
- ☐ _____
- ☐ _____

top priorities

_____

_____

_____

_____

_____

_____

_____

_____

_____

_____

three things I need to
give to God today...

1 _____

2 _____

3 _____

my prayer today is...

_____

_____

_____

_____

_____

_____

_____

_____

_____

_____

what is your "win" today?

_____

_____

_____

_____

Today Is Your Day

Therefore, my dear brothers and sisters, stand firm.
Let nothing move you. Always give yourselves fully to the work of the Lord,
because you know that your labor in the Lord is not in vain.

I CORINTHIANS 15:58 NIV

I am grateful for...

_____

_____

_____

_____

_____

to-do list	top priorities
☐ _____	_____
☐ _____	_____
☐ _____	_____
☐ _____	_____
☐ _____	_____
☐ _____	_____
☐ _____	_____
☐ _____	_____
☐ _____	_____
☐ _____	_____
☐ _____	_____
☐ _____	_____

three things I need to
give to God today...

1 _____

2 _____

3 _____

my prayer today is...

_____

_____

_____

_____

_____

_____

_____

_____

_____

_____

what is your "win" today?

_____

_____

_____

_____

_____

Today Is Your Day

Give all your worries and cares to God,
for He cares about you.
I PETER 5:7 NLT

I am grateful for...

_____
_____
_____
_____
_____

to-do list

- [ ] _____
- [ ] _____
- [ ] _____
- [ ] _____
- [ ] _____
- [ ] _____
- [ ] _____
- [ ] _____
- [ ] _____
- [ ] _____
- [ ] _____
- [ ] _____

top priorities

_____
_____
_____
_____
_____
_____
_____
_____
_____
_____

three things I need to
give to God today...

1
2
3

my prayer today is...

what is your "win" today?

Today Is Your Day

For God gave us a spirit not of fear
but of power and love and self-control.
II TIMOTHY 1:7

I am grateful for...

_____
_____
_____
_____
_____

to-do list

- ☐ _____
- ☐ _____
- ☐ _____
- ☐ _____
- ☐ _____
- ☐ _____
- ☐ _____
- ☐ _____
- ☐ _____
- ☐ _____
- ☐ _____
- ☐ _____

top priorities

_____
_____
_____
_____
_____
_____
_____
_____
_____
_____

three things I need to
give to God today...

1 _____
2 _____
3 _____

my prayer today is...

_____
_____
_____
_____
_____
_____
_____
_____
_____
_____

what is your "win" today?

_____
_____
_____
_____

Today Is Your Day

Do not be anxious about anything,
but in everything by prayer and supplication with thanksgiving
let your requests be made known to God.
PHILIPPIANS 4:6

I am grateful for...

_____
_____
_____
_____
_____

to-do list   top priorities

- ☐ _____   _____
- ☐ _____   _____
- ☐ _____   _____
- ☐ _____   _____
- ☐ _____   _____
- ☐ _____   _____
- ☐ _____   _____
- ☐ _____   _____
- ☐ _____   _____
- ☐ _____   _____
- ☐ _____   _____
- ☐ _____

three things I need to
give to God today...

1 _____
2 _____
3 _____

my prayer today is...

_____
_____
_____
_____
_____
_____
_____
_____
_____
_____
_____

what is your "win" today?

_____
_____
_____
_____

Today Is Your Day

And this is the confidence that we have toward him,
that if we ask anything according to his will he hears us.
And if we know that he hears us in whatever we ask,
we know that we have the requests that we have asked of him.
I JOHN 5:14–15

I am grateful for...

_____

_____

_____

_____

_____

to-do list	top priorities
☐ _____	_____
☐ _____	_____
☐ _____	_____
☐ _____	_____
☐ _____	_____
☐ _____	_____
☐ _____	_____
☐ _____	_____
☐ _____	_____
☐ _____	_____
☐ _____	

three things I need to
give to God today...

1
2
3

my prayer today is...

what is your "win" today?

Today Is Your Day

Be still before the LORD and wait patiently for him;
fret not yourself over the one who prospers in his way,
over the man who carries out evil devices! Refrain from anger,
and forsake wrath! Fret not yourself; it tends only to evil.

PSALM 37:7–8

I am grateful for...

_____
_____
_____
_____
_____

to-do list

- [ ] _____
- [ ] _____
- [ ] _____
- [ ] _____
- [ ] _____
- [ ] _____
- [ ] _____
- [ ] _____
- [ ] _____
- [ ] _____
- [ ] _____

top priorities

_____
_____
_____
_____
_____
_____
_____
_____
_____

three things I need to
give to God today...

1 _____
2 _____
3 _____

my prayer today is...

_____
_____
_____
_____
_____
_____
_____
_____
_____
_____

what is your "win" today?

_____
_____
_____
_____

you are
capable of
Amazing
things

Spreading Joy

This week, spend some time focusing on how you can be a light to others. Each day, focus on a different person or group of people to pray for. You may not even know what they need, but bring them to God in prayer. Every day, do a small act of kindness to bring joy to someone else. Smile as you pass someone on the street, shovel a neighbor's driveway, assist a coworker on a project, cook a meal for a friend . . . make an intentional choice to bless others without expecting anything in return. Find small ways this week to be Jesus to others. You might be surprised how much joy even a small gesture of kindness or thoughtfulness can bring to someone! This week, take the focus off yourself and put it on serving others by bringing them a little slice of joy!

habit tracker

HABIT	GOAL	MON	TUE	WED	THU	FRI	SAT	SUN

what are your dreams +
goals this week?

_____
_____
_____
_____
_____
_____

top 3 tasks for
the week ahead

1 _____
2 _____
3 _____

what is something fun
you are looking forward
to this week?

_____
_____
_____
_____
_____
_____

Today Is Your Day

Do nothing from selfish ambition or conceit, but in humility count others more significant than yourselves. Let each of you look not only to his own interests, but also to the interests of others.

PHILIPPIANS 2:3–4

I am grateful for...

_____
_____
_____
_____
_____

to-do list

- ☐ _____
- ☐ _____
- ☐ _____
- ☐ _____
- ☐ _____
- ☐ _____
- ☐ _____
- ☐ _____
- ☐ _____
- ☐ _____
- ☐ _____
- ☐ _____

top priorities

_____
_____
_____
_____
_____
_____
_____
_____
_____
_____

three things I need to
give to God today...

1 _____
2 _____
3 _____

my prayer today is...

_____
_____
_____
_____
_____
_____
_____
_____
_____
_____

what is your "win" today?

_____
_____
_____
_____

Today Is Your Day

Let us not become weary in doing good,
for at the proper time we will reap a harvest
if we do not give up.
GALATIANS 6:9 NIV

I am grateful for...

_____
_____
_____
_____
_____

to-do list

- ☐ _____
- ☐ _____
- ☐ _____
- ☐ _____
- ☐ _____
- ☐ _____
- ☐ _____
- ☐ _____
- ☐ _____
- ☐ _____
- ☐ _____
- ☐ _____

top priorities

_____
_____
_____
_____
_____
_____
_____
_____
_____
_____
_____

three things I need to
give to God today...

1 _____
2 _____
3 _____

my prayer today is...

_____
_____
_____
_____
_____
_____
_____
_____
_____
_____
_____

what is your "win" today?

_____
_____
_____
_____

Today Is Your Day

"'You shall love your neighbor as yourself.'
There is no other commandment greater than these."
MARK 12:31

I am grateful for...

_____
_____
_____
_____
_____

to-do list

- ☐ _____
- ☐ _____
- ☐ _____
- ☐ _____
- ☐ _____
- ☐ _____
- ☐ _____
- ☐ _____
- ☐ _____
- ☐ _____
- ☐ _____
- ☐ _____

top priorities

_____
_____
_____
_____
_____
_____
_____
_____
_____
_____
_____

three things I need to
give to God today...

1 _____
2 _____
3 _____

my prayer today is...

_____
_____
_____
_____
_____
_____
_____
_____
_____
_____

what is your "win" today?

_____
_____
_____
_____

Today Is Your Day

"Give, and it will be given to you."
LUKE 6:38 ESV

I am grateful for...

_____
_____
_____
_____
_____

to-do list

- ☐ _____
- ☐ _____
- ☐ _____
- ☐ _____
- ☐ _____
- ☐ _____
- ☐ _____
- ☐ _____
- ☐ _____
- ☐ _____
- ☐ _____
- ☐ _____

top priorities

_____
_____
_____
_____
_____
_____
_____
_____
_____
_____

three things I need to
give to God today...

1
2
3

my prayer today is...

what is your "win" today?

Today Is Your Day

As each has received a gift, use it to serve one another,
as good stewards of God's varied grace.
I PETER 4:10

I am grateful for...

_____

_____

_____

_____

_____

to-do list

- ☐ _____
- ☐ _____
- ☐ _____
- ☐ _____
- ☐ _____
- ☐ _____
- ☐ _____
- ☐ _____
- ☐ _____
- ☐ _____
- ☐ _____
- ☐ _____

top priorities

_____

_____

_____

_____

_____

_____

_____

_____

_____

_____

_____

three things I need to
give to God today...

1 _____

2 _____

3 _____

my prayer today is...

_____

_____

_____

_____

_____

_____

_____

_____

_____

_____

what is your "win" today?

_____

_____

_____

_____

Today Is Your Day

In all things I have shown you that by working hard in this way we
must help the weak and remember the words of the Lord Jesus,
how he himself said, "It is more blessed to give than to receive."
ACTS 20:35

I am grateful for...

_____

_____

_____

_____

_____

to-do list

- ☐ _____
- ☐ _____
- ☐ _____
- ☐ _____
- ☐ _____
- ☐ _____
- ☐ _____
- ☐ _____
- ☐ _____
- ☐ _____
- ☐ _____
- ☐ _____

top priorities

_____

_____

_____

_____

_____

_____

_____

_____

_____

_____

_____

_____

three things I need to
give to God today...

1
2
3

my prayer today is...

what is your "win" today?

Today Is Your Day

"In the same way, let your light shine before others,
so that they may see your good works and give glory
to your Father who is in heaven."

MATTHEW 5:16

I am grateful for...

_____

_____

_____

_____

_____

to-do list

- ☐ _____
- ☐ _____
- ☐ _____
- ☐ _____
- ☐ _____
- ☐ _____
- ☐ _____
- ☐ _____
- ☐ _____
- ☐ _____
- ☐ _____
- ☐ _____

top priorities

_____

_____

_____

_____

_____

_____

_____

_____

three things I need to
give to God today...

1
2
3

my prayer today is...

what is your "win" today?

be the girl who decided to go for it

Living Freely

This is the week of small actions and big rewards. When we have clutter in our minds and in our lives, we can become focused on the mess rather than living our best lives. This week, I want to encourage you to go through your junk drawers, closets, and the works! Determine what's no longer serving you, and donate it to someone who can use it. Do the same with what's been on your heart. Go to God in prayer, and just as you packed your physical things away, pack away what's been weighing on your mind into bags, then place them at the feet of Jesus. Let Him take what's no longer serving you and what's burdening your heart so you can live more freely. When you give it up, you have to really give it up. Then watch Him work wonders through what you've decided to let go, both personally and spiritually.

habit tracker

HABIT	GOAL	MON	TUE	WED	THU	FRI	SAT	SUN

what are your dreams +
goals this week?

_____
_____
_____
_____
_____
_____
_____

top 3 tasks for
the week ahead

1 _____
2 _____
3 _____

what is something fun
you are looking forward
to this week?

_____
_____
_____
_____
_____
_____
_____

Today Is Your Day

"Peace I leave with you; my peace I give to you.
Not as the world gives do I give to you. Let not your hearts be
troubled, neither let them be afraid."

JOHN 14:27

I am grateful for...

_____

_____

_____

_____

_____

to-do list

- ☐ _____
- ☐ _____
- ☐ _____
- ☐ _____
- ☐ _____
- ☐ _____
- ☐ _____
- ☐ _____
- ☐ _____
- ☐ _____
- ☐ _____
- ☐ _____

top priorities

_____

_____

_____

_____

_____

_____

_____

_____

_____

_____

three things I need to
give to God today...

1 _____

2 _____

3 _____

my prayer today is...

_____

_____

_____

_____

_____

_____

_____

_____

_____

what is your "win" today?

_____

_____

_____

_____

Today Is Your Day

So we do not lose heart. Though our outer self is wasting away, our inner self is being renewed day by day. For this light momentary affliction is preparing for us an eternal weight of glory beyond all comparison, as we look not to the things that are seen but to the things that are unseen. For the things that are seen are transient, but the things that are unseen are eternal.

II CORINTHIANS 4:16–18

I am grateful for...

---

to-do list

☐ _____
☐ _____
☐ _____
☐ _____
☐ _____
☐ _____
☐ _____
☐ _____
☐ _____

top priorities

_____
_____
_____
_____
_____
_____
_____
_____

three things I need to
give to God today...

1
2
3

my prayer today is...

what is your "win" today?

Today Is Your Day

Give all your worries to Him because He cares for you.

I PETER 5:7 NLV

I am grateful for...

_____

_____

_____

_____

_____

to-do list

- ☐ _____
- ☐ _____
- ☐ _____
- ☐ _____
- ☐ _____
- ☐ _____
- ☐ _____
- ☐ _____
- ☐ _____
- ☐ _____
- ☐ _____
- ☐ _____

top priorities

_____

_____

_____

_____

_____

_____

_____

_____

three things I need to
give to God today...

1 _____
2 _____
3 _____

my prayer today is...

_____
_____
_____
_____
_____
_____
_____
_____
_____
_____

what is your "win" today?

_____
_____
_____
_____

Today Is Your Day

Giving thanks always and for everything to God the Father
in the name of our Lord Jesus Christ.

EPHESIANS 5:20

I am grateful for...

_____

_____

_____

_____

_____

to-do list

- [ ] _____
- [ ] _____
- [ ] _____
- [ ] _____
- [ ] _____
- [ ] _____
- [ ] _____
- [ ] _____
- [ ] _____
- [ ] _____
- [ ] _____
- [ ] _____

top priorities

_____

_____

_____

_____

_____

_____

_____

_____

_____

_____

_____

three things I need to
give to God today...

1 _____
2 _____
3 _____

my prayer today is...

_____
_____
_____
_____
_____
_____
_____
_____
_____
_____
_____

what is your "win" today?

_____
_____
_____
_____

Today Is Your Day

Anxiety in a man's heart weighs him down,
but a good word makes him glad.
PROVERBS 12:25

I am grateful for...

_____
_____
_____
_____
_____

to-do list

- ☐ _____
- ☐ _____
- ☐ _____
- ☐ _____
- ☐ _____
- ☐ _____
- ☐ _____
- ☐ _____
- ☐ _____
- ☐ _____
- ☐ _____
- ☐ _____

top priorities

_____
_____
_____
_____
_____
_____
_____
_____
_____

three things I need to
give to God today...

1 _____
2 _____
3 _____

my prayer today is...

_____
_____
_____
_____
_____
_____
_____
_____
_____
_____

what is your "win" today?

_____
_____
_____
_____

Today Is Your Day

"You will seek me and find me
when you seek me with all your heart."
JEREMIAH 29:13

I am grateful for...

_____
_____
_____
_____
_____

to-do list

- [ ] _____
- [ ] _____
- [ ] _____
- [ ] _____
- [ ] _____
- [ ] _____
- [ ] _____
- [ ] _____
- [ ] _____
- [ ] _____
- [ ] _____
- [ ] _____

top priorities

_____
_____
_____
_____
_____
_____
_____
_____

three things I need to
give to God today...

1 _____
2 _____
3 _____

my prayer today is...

_____
_____
_____
_____
_____
_____
_____
_____
_____
_____

what is your "win" today?

_____
_____
_____
_____

Today Is Your Day

"Therefore do not be anxious about tomorrow,
for tomorrow will be anxious for itself.
Sufficient for the day is its own trouble."
MATTHEW 6:34

I am grateful for...

_____

_____

_____

_____

_____

to-do list	top priorities
☐ _____	_____
☐ _____	_____
☐ _____	_____
☐ _____	_____
☐ _____	_____
☐ _____	_____
☐ _____	_____
☐ _____	_____
☐ _____	_____
☐ _____	_____
☐ _____	_____
☐ _____	_____

three things I need to
give to God today...

1 _____
2 _____
3 _____

my prayer today is...

_____
_____
_____
_____
_____
_____
_____
_____
_____
_____

what is your "win" today?

_____
_____
_____
_____

say yes!
to new
adventures

Being Present

This week has a big challenge: to spend time on other activities rather than on screens. That means your phone, computer, TV—everything! (Not including work, of course!) Instead, look up from the screen. What do you see? Maybe it's your family or the natural world that God created outside your window. During this time, allow yourself to focus on what God has created and what or whom He's blessed you with. Take a walk in nature, go see a friend, spend time with your family, take up a new hobby, or bake those cookies you have been putting off. Whatever it is, try moving away from technology and see how you feel. Instead of looking for acceptance and worth in social media or getting lost in a TV show, free yourself from what's pulled you in too many times before. This week, live in the present, and don't miss out on the good stuff! I bet you'll find a new sense of freedom you've never experienced before!

habit tracker

HABIT	GOAL	MON	TUE	WED	THU	FRI	SAT	SUN

what are your dreams +
goals this week?

_____

top 3 tasks for
the week ahead

1 _____
2 _____
3 _____

what is something fun
you are looking forward
to this week?

_____

Today Is Your Day

Finally, brothers and sisters, whatever is true,
whatever is noble, whatever is right, whatever is pure,
whatever is lovely, whatever is admirable—
if anything is excellent or praiseworthy—think about such things.
PHILIPPIANS 4:8 NIV

I am grateful for...

to-do list

- [ ]
- [ ]
- [ ]
- [ ]
- [ ]
- [ ]
- [ ]
- [ ]
- [ ]
- [ ]
- [ ]

top priorities

three things I need to
give to God today...

1 _____
2 _____
3 _____

my prayer today is...

_____
_____
_____
_____
_____
_____
_____
_____
_____
_____

what is your "win" today?

_____
_____
_____
_____

Today Is Your Day

"Sell your possessions, and give to the needy. Provide yourselves with moneybags that do not grow old, with a treasure in the heavens that does not fail, where no thief approaches and no moth destroys. For where your treasure is, there will your heart be also."

LUKE 12:33–34

I am grateful for...

_____

_____

_____

_____

_____

to-do list

- ☐ _____
- ☐ _____
- ☐ _____
- ☐ _____
- ☐ _____
- ☐ _____
- ☐ _____
- ☐ _____
- ☐ _____
- ☐ _____
- ☐ _____

top priorities

_____

_____

_____

_____

_____

_____

_____

_____

three things I need to
give to God today...

1
2
3

my prayer today is...

what is your "win" today?

Today Is Your Day

I keep my eyes always on the LORD.
With Him at my right hand, I will not be shaken.
PSALM 16:8 NIV

I am grateful for...

_____
_____
_____
_____
_____

to-do list

- ☐ _____
- ☐ _____
- ☐ _____
- ☐ _____
- ☐ _____
- ☐ _____
- ☐ _____
- ☐ _____
- ☐ _____
- ☐ _____
- ☐ _____
- ☐ _____

top priorities

_____
_____
_____
_____
_____
_____
_____
_____
_____
_____

three things I need to
give to God today...

1 _____
2 _____
3 _____

my prayer today is...

_____
_____
_____
_____
_____
_____
_____
_____
_____
_____

what is your "win" today?

_____
_____
_____
_____

Today Is Your Day

Every good gift and every perfect gift is from above,
coming down from the Father of lights, with whom there is
no variation or shadow due to change.

JAMES 1:17

I am grateful for...

_____
_____
_____
_____
_____

to-do list

- [ ] _____
- [ ] _____
- [ ] _____
- [ ] _____
- [ ] _____
- [ ] _____
- [ ] _____
- [ ] _____
- [ ] _____
- [ ] _____
- [ ] _____
- [ ] _____

top priorities

_____
_____
_____
_____
_____
_____
_____
_____
_____
_____
_____

three things I need to
give to God today...

1 _____
2 _____
3 _____

my prayer today is...

_____
_____
_____
_____
_____
_____
_____
_____
_____

what is your "win" today?

_____
_____
_____
_____

Today Is Your Day

Do not be conformed to this world, but be transformed by the renewal of your mind, that by testing you may discern what is the will of God, what is good and acceptable and perfect.
ROMANS 12:2

I am grateful for...

_____

_____

_____

_____

_____

to-do list

- ☐ _____
- ☐ _____
- ☐ _____
- ☐ _____
- ☐ _____
- ☐ _____
- ☐ _____
- ☐ _____
- ☐ _____
- ☐ _____
- ☐ _____
- ☐ _____

top priorities

_____

_____

_____

_____

_____

_____

_____

_____

_____

_____

three things I need to
give to God today...

1
2
3

my prayer today is...

what is your "win" today?

Today Is Your Day

You were chosen to be free. . . .
Live this free life by loving and helping others.
GALATIANS 5:13 NLV

I am grateful for...

_____
_____
_____
_____
_____

to-do list

- ☐ _____
- ☐ _____
- ☐ _____
- ☐ _____
- ☐ _____
- ☐ _____
- ☐ _____
- ☐ _____
- ☐ _____
- ☐ _____
- ☐ _____
- ☐ _____

top priorities

_____
_____
_____
_____
_____
_____
_____
_____
_____
_____

three things I need to
give to God today...

1 _____
2 _____
3 _____

my prayer today is...

_____
_____
_____
_____
_____
_____
_____
_____
_____
_____

what is your "win" today?

_____
_____
_____
_____

Today Is Your Day

Even though I walk through the valley of the shadow of death,
I will fear no evil, for you are with me;
your rod and your staff, they comfort me.
PSALM 23:4

I am grateful for...

_____
_____
_____
_____
_____

to-do list

- ☐ _____
- ☐ _____
- ☐ _____
- ☐ _____
- ☐ _____
- ☐ _____
- ☐ _____
- ☐ _____
- ☐ _____
- ☐ _____
- ☐ _____
- ☐ _____

top priorities

_____
_____
_____
_____
_____
_____
_____
_____
_____
_____

three things I need to
give to God today...

1 _____
2 _____
3 _____

my prayer today is...

_____
_____
_____
_____
_____
_____
_____
_____
_____
_____

what is your "win" today?

_____
_____
_____
_____

she
remembered
who she was
and the
game
changed

Being Present

What does success look like to you? We can often strive so hard to impress others or please ourselves. This week, remind yourself that you can't be everything to everyone. Take a look at where your heart is versus where your hustle is. Are you striving for success, recognition, or a paycheck? Or are you pursuing what you love doing and living out what God made you to do? Set aside moments this week to reflect on what you're striving for or struggling with, and pray for God to reveal what direction He wants you to go. It may take days, months, or years for His plans for you to come to fruition, but rest in the peace of knowing you are always exactly where you're supposed to be to get to where you're meant to go. You can't mess up because He's by your side, and it's all a part of His greater plan and your journey. When you get that nudge from the Lord, go in that direction, even if it's something you feel like you can't do. Listen and obey. This week, be all in, and be strong and courageous!

habit tracker

HABIT	GOAL	MON	TUE	WED	THU	FRI	SAT	SUN

what are your dreams +
goals this week?

_____
_____
_____
_____
_____

top 3 tasks for
the week ahead

1 _____
2 _____
3 _____

what is something fun
you are looking forward
to this week?

_____
_____
_____
_____
_____
_____

Today Is Your Day

Have I not commanded you? Be strong and courageous.
Do not be frightened, and do not be dismayed,
for the LORD your God is with you wherever you go.
JOSHUA 1:9

I am grateful for...

_____
_____
_____
_____
_____

to-do list

- ☐ _____
- ☐ _____
- ☐ _____
- ☐ _____
- ☐ _____
- ☐ _____
- ☐ _____
- ☐ _____
- ☐ _____
- ☐ _____
- ☐ _____
- ☐ _____

top priorities

_____
_____
_____
_____
_____
_____
_____
_____
_____
_____
_____

three things I need to
give to God today...

1
2
3

my prayer today is...

what is your "win" today?

Today Is Your Day

Keep your life free from love of money,
and be content with what you have, for he has said,
"I will never leave you nor forsake you."
HEBREWS 13:5

I am grateful for...

_____
_____
_____
_____
_____

to-do list

- [ ] _____
- [ ] _____
- [ ] _____
- [ ] _____
- [ ] _____
- [ ] _____
- [ ] _____
- [ ] _____
- [ ] _____
- [ ] _____
- [ ] _____
- [ ] _____

top priorities

_____
_____
_____
_____
_____
_____
_____
_____
_____
_____
_____

three things I need to
give to God today...

1 _____

2 _____

3 _____

my prayer today is...

_____

_____

_____

_____

_____

_____

_____

_____

_____

_____

what is your "win" today?

_____

_____

_____

_____

Today Is Your Day

"My sheep hear my voice, and I know them,
and they follow me."
JOHN 10:27

I am grateful for...

_____

_____

_____

_____

_____

to-do list

- ☐ _____
- ☐ _____
- ☐ _____
- ☐ _____
- ☐ _____
- ☐ _____
- ☐ _____
- ☐ _____
- ☐ _____
- ☐ _____
- ☐ _____
- ☐ _____

top priorities

_____

_____

_____

_____

_____

_____

_____

_____

_____

_____

three things I need to
give to God today...

1 _____
2 _____
3 _____

my prayer today is...

_____
_____
_____
_____
_____
_____
_____
_____
_____
_____

what is your "win" today?

_____
_____
_____
_____

Today Is Your Day

Trust in the Lord with all your heart, and do not trust
in your own understanding. Agree with Him in all your ways,
and He will make your paths straight.
PROVERBS 3:5–6 NLV

I am grateful for...

_____
_____
_____
_____
_____

to-do list

- [ ] _____
- [ ] _____
- [ ] _____
- [ ] _____
- [ ] _____
- [ ] _____
- [ ] _____
- [ ] _____
- [ ] _____
- [ ] _____
- [ ] _____
- [ ] _____

top priorities

_____
_____
_____
_____
_____
_____
_____
_____
_____
_____

three things I need to
give to God today...

1
2
3

my prayer today is...

what is your "win" today?

Today Is Your Day

Whatever you do, work heartily,
as for the Lord and not for men.
COLOSSIANS 3:23

I am grateful for...

_____
_____
_____
_____
_____

to-do list

- ☐ _____
- ☐ _____
- ☐ _____
- ☐ _____
- ☐ _____
- ☐ _____
- ☐ _____
- ☐ _____
- ☐ _____
- ☐ _____
- ☐ _____
- ☐ _____

top priorities

_____
_____
_____
_____
_____
_____
_____
_____
_____

three things I need to
give to God today...

1 _____
2 _____
3 _____

my prayer today is...

_____
_____
_____
_____
_____
_____
_____
_____
_____
_____
_____

what is your "win" today?

_____
_____
_____
_____
_____

Today Is Your Day

"No one can serve two masters, for either he will hate the one and love the other, or he will be devoted to the one and despise the other. You cannot serve God and money."

MATTHEW 6:24

I am grateful for...

_____

_____

_____

_____

_____

to-do list	top priorities
☐ _____	_____
☐ _____	_____
☐ _____	_____
☐ _____	_____
☐ _____	_____
☐ _____	_____
☐ _____	_____
☐ _____	_____
☐ _____	_____
☐ _____	_____
☐ _____	_____
☐ _____	

three things I need to
give to God today...

1
2
3

my prayer today is...

what is your "win" today?

Today Is Your Day

"Yes, I am the vine; you are the branches.
Those who remain in Me, and I in them, will produce much fruit.
For apart from Me you can do nothing."

JOHN 15:5 NLT

I am grateful for...

_____
_____
_____
_____
_____

to-do list

- [ ] _____
- [ ] _____
- [ ] _____
- [ ] _____
- [ ] _____
- [ ] _____
- [ ] _____
- [ ] _____
- [ ] _____
- [ ] _____
- [ ] _____
- [ ] _____

top priorities

_____
_____
_____
_____
_____
_____
_____
_____

three things I need to
give to God today...

1 _____
2 _____
3 _____

my prayer today is...

_____
_____
_____
_____
_____
_____
_____
_____
_____
_____
_____

what is your "win" today?

_____
_____
_____
_____
_____

doubt kills
more dreams
than failure
ever will

Making Time for You

This week, take time for you! You may be bogged down with work, family, tasks—and all the things—but schedule some time just for you! Take the pressure off of yourself to accomplish everything else, and carve out some time for rest. Remember, you don't have to do it all or have it all figured out. Too many times we put ourselves last or settle for what's leftover, but you are important too! Whether that's painting your nails, taking a long bath, enjoying a trip to your favorite store, attending a fun class, winding down with a good book—you name it! Go do it! While you're enjoying what you love doing, be still and listen for God. In the moments away from the hustle and bustle, it's easier to hear Him. Take some moments to talk to Him, tell Him what's on your heart and mind, and release it all to Him . . . then receive His supernatural peace.

habit tracker

HABIT	GOAL	MON	TUE	WED	THU	FRI	SAT	SUN

what are your dreams +
goals this week?

_____
_____
_____
_____
_____
_____

top 3 tasks for
the week ahead

1 _____
2 _____
3 _____

what is something fun
you are looking forward
to this week?

_____
_____
_____
_____
_____
_____

Today Is Your Day

Oh give thanks to the Lord, for he is good,
for his steadfast love endures forever!
PSALM 107:1

I am grateful for...

_____
_____
_____
_____
_____

to-do list

- ☐ _____
- ☐ _____
- ☐ _____
- ☐ _____
- ☐ _____
- ☐ _____
- ☐ _____
- ☐ _____
- ☐ _____
- ☐ _____
- ☐ _____
- ☐ _____

top priorities

_____
_____
_____
_____
_____
_____
_____
_____
_____
_____

three things I need to
give to God today...

1
2
3

my prayer today is...

what is your "win" today?

Today Is Your Day

"Come to me, all who labor and are heavy laden,
and I will give you rest. Take my yoke upon you, and learn from
me, for I am gentle and lowly in heart, and you will find rest for
your souls. For my yoke is easy, and my burden is light."
MATTHEW 11:28–30

I am grateful for...

to-do list

- [ ]
- [ ]
- [ ]
- [ ]
- [ ]
- [ ]
- [ ]
- [ ]
- [ ]
- [ ]
- [ ]

top priorities

three things I need to
give to God today...

1 _____

2 _____

3 _____

my prayer today is...

_____

_____

_____

_____

_____

_____

_____

_____

_____

_____

what is your "win" today?

_____

_____

_____

_____

Today Is Your Day

"Be still, and know that I am God."
PSALM 46:10

I am grateful for...

_____
_____
_____
_____
_____

to-do list

- [ ] _____
- [ ] _____
- [ ] _____
- [ ] _____
- [ ] _____
- [ ] _____
- [ ] _____
- [ ] _____
- [ ] _____
- [ ] _____
- [ ] _____
- [ ] _____

top priorities

_____
_____
_____
_____
_____
_____
_____
_____
_____
_____
_____

three things I need to
give to God today...

1 _____
2 _____
3 _____

my prayer today is...

_____
_____
_____
_____
_____
_____
_____
_____
_____
_____

what is your "win" today?

_____
_____
_____
_____

Today Is Your Day

And he said, "My presence will go with you,
and I will give you rest."
EXODUS 33:14

I am grateful for...

_____
_____
_____
_____
_____

to-do list

- [ ] _____
- [ ] _____
- [ ] _____
- [ ] _____
- [ ] _____
- [ ] _____
- [ ] _____
- [ ] _____
- [ ] _____
- [ ] _____
- [ ] _____
- [ ] _____

top priorities

_____
_____
_____
_____
_____
_____
_____
_____
_____
_____
_____

three things I need to
give to God today...

1
2
3

my prayer today is...

what is your "win" today?

Today Is Your Day

We live by faith, not by sight.
II CORINTHIANS 5:7 NIV

I am grateful for...

_____
_____
_____
_____
_____

to-do list

- ☐ _____
- ☐ _____
- ☐ _____
- ☐ _____
- ☐ _____
- ☐ _____
- ☐ _____
- ☐ _____
- ☐ _____
- ☐ _____
- ☐ _____
- ☐ _____

top priorities

_____
_____
_____
_____
_____
_____
_____
_____
_____
_____
_____

three things I need to
give to God today...

1 _____

2 _____

3 _____

my prayer today is...

_____

_____

_____

_____

_____

_____

_____

_____

_____

_____

_____

_____

what is your "win" today?

_____

_____

_____

_____

_____

Today Is Your Day

Again Jesus spoke to them, saying,
"I am the light of the world. Whoever follows me will not
walk in darkness, but will have the light of life."
JOHN 8:12

I am grateful for...

_____
_____
_____
_____
_____

to-do list

- [ ] _____
- [ ] _____
- [ ] _____
- [ ] _____
- [ ] _____
- [ ] _____
- [ ] _____
- [ ] _____
- [ ] _____
- [ ] _____
- [ ] _____
- [ ] _____

top priorities

_____
_____
_____
_____
_____
_____
_____
_____
_____

three things I need to
give to God today...

1 _____
2 _____
3 _____

my prayer today is...

_____
_____
_____
_____
_____
_____
_____
_____
_____
_____

what is your "win" today?

_____
_____
_____
_____

Today Is Your Day

And on the seventh day God finished his work that he had done,
and he rested on the seventh day from all his work that he had done.
GENESIS 2:2

I am grateful for...

_____
_____
_____
_____
_____

to-do list

- [ ] _____
- [ ] _____
- [ ] _____
- [ ] _____
- [ ] _____
- [ ] _____
- [ ] _____
- [ ] _____
- [ ] _____
- [ ] _____
- [ ] _____
- [ ] _____

top priorities

_____
_____
_____
_____
_____
_____
_____
_____
_____
_____

three things I need to
give to God today...

1
2
3

my prayer today is...

what is your "win" today?

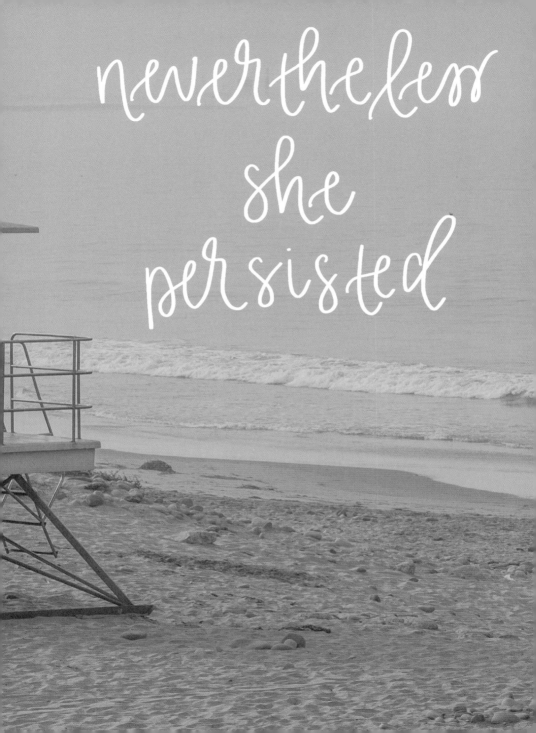

Time to Celebrate!

This week, celebrate how far you've come! In this journal, look back at each week and the goals you set for yourself. Did you accomplish them, or are they still in the works? This is a good time to reassess what's important, what's urgent, and what can wait. But through it all, give yourself grace. Remove the pressure to always be more and do more. It's okay not to have accomplished everything over the past weeks, but celebrate what you have accomplished, no matter how big or how small! You've made progress, and that's what matters. What do you hope to focus on next? Big plans? More rest? Blessing others? You may have enjoyed the weeks when you put away your phone or tried something new, and you can continue that practice! In the following weeks, go confidently in the direction where God is leading you, and be strong and courageous!

habit tracker

HABIT	GOAL	MON	TUE	WED	THU	FRI	SAT	SUN

what are your dreams +
goals this week?

_____
_____
_____
_____
_____
_____

top 3 tasks for
the week ahead

1 _____
2 _____
3 _____

what is something fun
you are looking forward
to this week?

_____
_____
_____
_____
_____
_____

Today Is Your Day

Jesus looked at them and said,
"With man it is impossible, but not with God.
For all things are possible with God."
MARK 10:27

I am grateful for...

_____
_____
_____
_____
_____
_____

to-do list

- [ ] _____
- [ ] _____
- [ ] _____
- [ ] _____
- [ ] _____
- [ ] _____
- [ ] _____
- [ ] _____
- [ ] _____
- [ ] _____
- [ ] _____
- [ ] _____

top priorities

_____
_____
_____
_____
_____
_____
_____
_____
_____
_____

three things I need to
give to God today...

1
2
3

my prayer today is...

what is your "win" today?

Today Is Your Day

For by grace you have been saved through faith.
And this is not your own doing; it is the gift of God,
not a result of works, so that no one may boast.
EPHESIANS 2:8–9

I am grateful for...

_____
_____
_____
_____
_____

to-do list

☐ _____
☐ _____
☐ _____
☐ _____
☐ _____
☐ _____
☐ _____
☐ _____
☐ _____
☐ _____
☐ _____
☐ _____

top priorities

_____
_____
_____
_____
_____
_____
_____
_____
_____

three things I need to
give to God today...

1 _____
2 _____
3 _____

my prayer today is...

_____
_____
_____
_____
_____
_____
_____
_____
_____
_____
_____

what is your "win" today?

_____
_____
_____
_____

Today Is Your Day

For everything there is a season,
and a time for every matter under heaven.
ECCLESIASTES 3:1

I am grateful for...

_____

_____

_____

_____

_____

to-do list

- [ ] _____
- [ ] _____
- [ ] _____
- [ ] _____
- [ ] _____
- [ ] _____
- [ ] _____
- [ ] _____
- [ ] _____
- [ ] _____
- [ ] _____
- [ ] _____

top priorities

_____

_____

_____

_____

_____

_____

_____

_____

_____

_____

three things I need to
give to God today...

1 _____
2 _____
3 _____

my prayer today is...

_____
_____
_____
_____
_____
_____
_____
_____
_____
_____
_____

what is your "win" today?

_____
_____
_____
_____

Today Is Your Day

The LORD is my strength and my shield; in him my heart trusts,
and I am helped; my heart exults,
and with my song I give thanks to him.
PSALM 28:7

I am grateful for...

_____

_____

_____

_____

_____

to-do list

☐ _____
☐ _____
☐ _____
☐ _____
☐ _____
☐ _____
☐ _____
☐ _____
☐ _____
☐ _____
☐ _____
☐ _____

top priorities

_____
_____
_____
_____
_____
_____
_____
_____
_____
_____

three things I need to
give to God today...

1
2
3

my prayer today is...

what is your "win" today?

Day 04

Today Is Your Day

But when he saw the wind, he was afraid,
and beginning to sink he cried out, "Lord, save me."
Jesus immediately reached out his hand and took hold of him,
saying to him, "O you of little faith, why did you doubt?"
MATTHEW 14:30–31

I am grateful for...

_____

_____

_____

_____

_____

to-do list

- ☐ _____
- ☐ _____
- ☐ _____
- ☐ _____
- ☐ _____
- ☐ _____
- ☐ _____
- ☐ _____
- ☐ _____
- ☐ _____
- ☐ _____

top priorities

_____

_____

_____

_____

_____

_____

_____

_____

_____

three things I need to
give to God today...

1
2
3

my prayer today is...

what is your "win" today?

Today Is Your Day

This is the day that the LORD has made;
let us rejoice and be glad in it.
PSALM 118:24

I am grateful for...

_____
_____
_____
_____
_____

to-do list   top priorities

☐ _____   _____
☐ _____   _____
☐ _____   _____
☐ _____   _____
☐ _____   _____
☐ _____   _____
☐ _____   _____
☐ _____   _____
☐ _____   _____
☐ _____   _____
☐ _____   _____
☐ _____

three things I need to
give to God today...

1 _____
2 _____
3 _____

my prayer today is...

_____
_____
_____
_____
_____
_____
_____
_____
_____
_____

what is your "win" today?

_____
_____
_____
_____

Today Is Your Day

You can make many plans,
but the LORD's purpose will prevail.
PROVERBS 19:21 NLT

I am grateful for...

_____
_____
_____
_____
_____

to-do list

- [ ] _____
- [ ] _____
- [ ] _____
- [ ] _____
- [ ] _____
- [ ] _____
- [ ] _____
- [ ] _____
- [ ] _____
- [ ] _____
- [ ] _____
- [ ] _____

top priorities

_____
_____
_____
_____
_____
_____
_____
_____

three things I need to
give to God today...

1 _____
2 _____
3 _____

my prayer today is...

_____
_____
_____
_____
_____
_____
_____
_____
_____
_____

what is your "win" today?

_____
_____
_____
_____

YOU GOT THIS

90 Devotions to Equip + Empower
hardworking women

M E L I S S A   H O R V A T H

GO FOR IT

BOLDLY LIVE THE LIFE
GOD CREATED FOR YOU

M E L I S S A   H O R V A T H

Want more encouragement from Melissa?

You can find her devotionals,
You've Got This and *Go For It,*
and other gifts on dayspring.com,
as well as in several retail
stores near you.

About the Author

MELISSA HORVATH began Sweet Water Décor in her basement in 2014; nine months later, she was working her business full-time. She encourages others through her home décor products, well-chosen words, and unique hand lettering. She's been featured in countless publications and networks, was one of Amazon's Women-Owned Businesses to watch in 2018, and resides in Pennsylvania with her husband and three children.

you are strong + coura
g + courageous · you are
· you are strong + coura
ng + courageous · you are
s · you are strong + cour
ng + courageous · you ar
s · you are strong + cour
ong + courageous · you ar
us · you are strong + cour
ong + courageous · you a
us · you are strong + cour
ong + courageous · you

u are strong + courageo
courageous · you are st
u are strong + courageo
courageous · you are st
ou are strong + courage
+ courageous · you are s
you are strong + courage
+ courageous · you are s
you are strong + courag
l + courageous · you are o
you are strong + courag
g + courageous · you are